I FEEL A BIT WEAK, GETAFIX ...

NO, OBELIX! YOU ARE NOT HAVING ANY MAGIC POTION! YOU KNOW VERY WELL YOU FELL INTO THE CAULDRON WHEN YOU WERE A BABY, AND IT HAD A PERMANENT EFFECT ON YOU!

GOSCINNY AND UDERZO
PRESENT
An Asterix Adventure

ASTERIX
AND THE
FALLING SKY

Written and Illustrated by ALBERT UDERZO

Translated by Anthea Bell *and* Derek Hockridge

ORION

For my brother Bruno, to whom I owe everything.

Bruno (1920-2004) and Albert Uderzo in 1942

Bruno Uderzo was Albert's elder brother. There were seven years between them. It was Bruno who, recognising his younger brother's budding talent, first took him to see a Parisian publisher. That was in the summer of 1940, and Albert was thirteen years old.

Respect, affection and shared interests united the two brothers.

GAULISH VILLAGE

COMPENDIUM

LAUDANUM

AQUARIUM

TOTORUM

ARMORICA

BELGICA

LUTETIA

GAUL
(ROMAN CONQUEST)
50 BC

CELTICA

PROVINCIA

AQUITANIA

THE YEAR IS 50 BC. GAUL IS ENTIRELY OCCUPIED BY THE
ROMANS. WELL, NOT ENTIRELY ... ONE SMALL VILLAGE OF
INDOMITABLE GAULS STILL HOLDS OUT AGAINST THE INVADERS.
AND LIFE IS NOT EASY FOR THE ROMAN LEGIONARIES WHO
GARRISON THE FORTIFIED CAMPS OF TOTORUM, AQUARIUM,
LAUDANUM AND COMPENDIUM ...

5

6

7

8

11

15

17

18

19

20

21

25

26

31

* BULL'S-EYE IN GALLO-ROMAN TIMES.

39

41

42

43

44

46

"In this book I would like to pay tribute to the great creations of Tadsilweny... sorry, I mean the great creations of Walt Disney who, famous and amazing druid that he was, allowed some of his colleagues, myself included, to fall into the cauldron of a potion of which he alone knew the magical secret."

Albert Uderzo

Original title: *Le Ciel Lui Tombe Sur La Tête*
Original edition © 2005 Les Éditions Albert René/Goscinny-Uderzo
English translation © 2005 Les Éditions Albert René/Goscinny-Uderzo

Exclusive Licensee: Orion Publishing Group
Translators: Anthea Bell and Derek Hockridge
Typography: Bryony Newhouse
Inking: Frédéric Mébarki
Colour work: Thierry Mébarki
Co-ordination: Studio 56

The right of Goscinny-Uderzo to be identified as the author of this work has been asserted by them in accordance with the Copyright, Designs and Patents Act 1988.

Hardback edition first published in Great Britain in 2005 by Orion Books Ltd, Orion House, 5 Upper St Martin's Lane, London WC2H 9EA

Printed in Italy

http://gb.asterix.com
www.orionbooks.co.uk

A CIP catalogue record for this book is available from the British Library

ISBN 0 75827 301 6

Distributed in the United States of America by Sterling Publishing Co. Inc., 387 Park Avenue South, New York, NY 10016